STAR WARS®
VADER'S QUEST

script
DARKO MACAN

art
DAVE GIBBONS

colors
ANGUS MCKIE

lettering
DAVE GIBBONS

cover art
DAVE GIBBONS &
ANGUS McKIE

TITAN BOOKS

publisher
MIKE RICHARDSON

series editor
PEET JANES

collection editor
CHRIS WARNER

collection designer
JEREMY PERKINS

art director
MARK COX

Special thanks to Allan Kausch and Lucy Autrey Wilson
at Lucas Licensing.

STAR WARS®: VADER'S QUEST

Published by Titan Books, a division of Titan Publishing Group Ltd. by arrangement
with Dark Horse Comics, Inc.

This book collects issues one through four of the Dark Horse
comic-book series STAR WARS®: VADER'S QUEST.

**Published by
Titan Books
144 Southwark St.
London SE1 0UP**

First edition: January 2000
ISBN: 1 84023 149 1

1 3 5 7 9 10 8 6 4 2
Printed in Canada

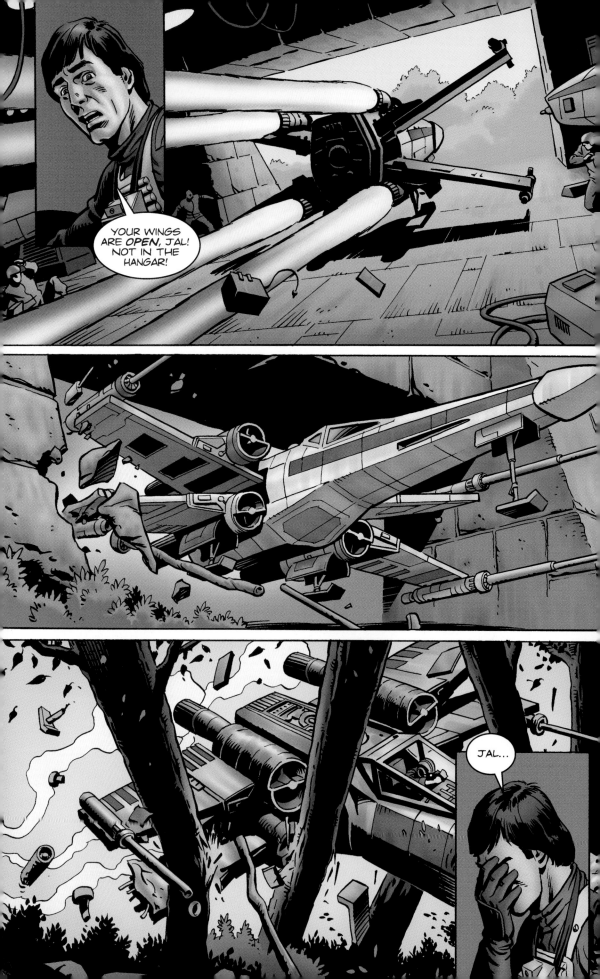

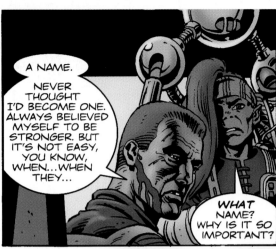

A NAME. NEVER THOUGHT I'D BECOME ONE. ALWAYS BELIEVED MYSELF TO BE STRONGER. BUT IT'S NOT EASY, YOU KNOW, WHEN...WHEN THEY...

WHAT NAME? WHY IS IT SO IMPORTANT?

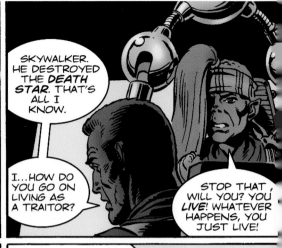

SKYWALKER. HE DESTROYED THE *DEATH STAR.* THAT'S ALL I KNOW.

I...HOW DO YOU GO ON LIVING AS A TRAITOR?

STOP THAT, WILL YOU? YOU *LIVE!* WHATEVER HAPPENS, YOU JUST LIVE!

HEY, YOU AREN'T THE PLANT, BY ANY CHANCE?

EXCUSE ME?

THE PLANT! SENT HERE TO PLANT FALSE INFORMATION, MAKE VADER FLIP? I MEAN, YOU *ARE* A LONG WAY FROM HOME.

NO, NO...I *AM* HOME!

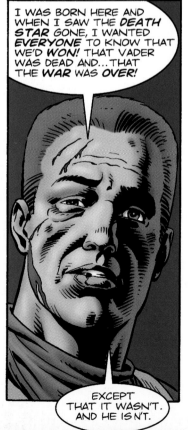

I WAS BORN HERE AND WHEN I SAW THE *DEATH STAR* GONE, I WANTED *EVERYONE* TO KNOW THAT WE'D *WON!* THAT VADER WAS DEAD AND...THAT THE *WAR* WAS *OVER!*

EXCEPT THAT IT WASN'T. AND HE ISN'T.

THERE'S ONLY ONE WAY WAR ENDS FOR A SOLDIER.

I KNOW. NOW I KNOW.

I'M SORRY.

I'M NOT.

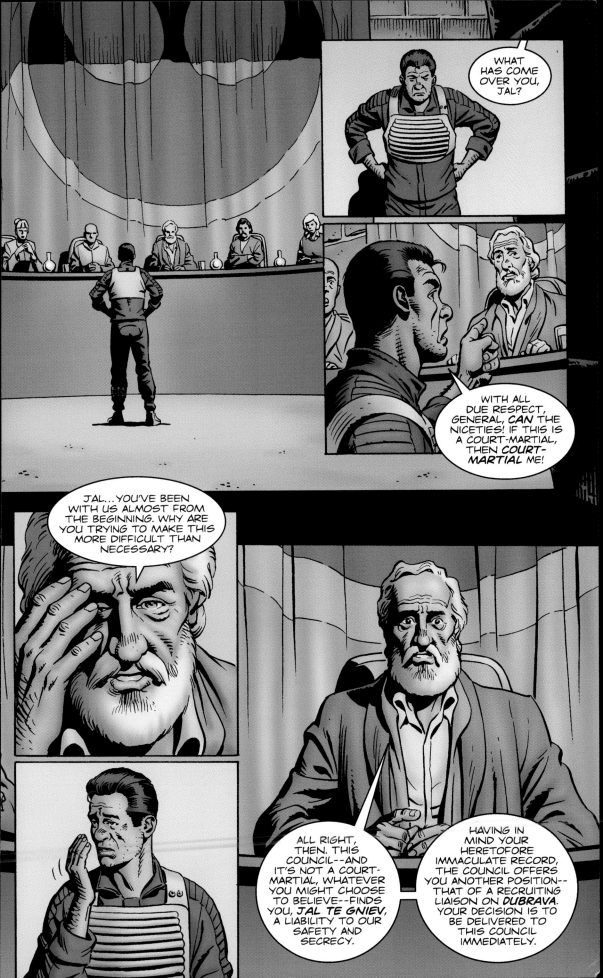

MISTRESS!

I CAME AS SOON AS I COULD, MISTRESS! ARE YOU ALL RIGHT?

I'VE BEEN BETTER, *BEESIX!* LET'S JUST SAY I'M GLAD MOST OF MY NERVE ENDINGS ARE ALREADY DEAD!

I'LL GET YOU OUT OF THERE IN NO TIME, MISTRESS! TOO BAD ABOUT FORDEE, HUH?

WHAT'S IT TO YOU?

I'VE BEEN TOLD, SIR, YOU ARE THE ONE TO CONTACT IF I'M TO JOIN THE REBELLION...SIR!

YOU WANT TO BE A PILOT! *HAHAHA!* IS THAT IT, KID?

BOBEK, SIR, AND... YES, I WANT TO FLY FOR THE REBELLION!

LOOK HERE, BOYS! THIS IS THE NEXT *STAR* FOR THE REBELLION! NOW THEY CAN KICK OUT *ANOTHER* VETERAN!

BUT I'LL HAVE TO PUT YOU THROUGH A TEST FIRST, KID!

YES, SIR! I'M READY, SIR!

COME WITH ME, NO REASON WHY WE CAN'T DO IT NOW!

DO YOU STILL *TRUST* THE REBELLION, KID? *DO YOU?*

WHY SO GLOOMY, HANDSOME?

THIRTY-ONE MISSIONS...

WHY, SIR? I DON'T UNDER-STAND!

OF COURSE YOU DON'T UNDERSTAND! BECAUSE YOU ARE *STUPID!*

LIKE *I* WAS!

THE BEST YEARS OF MY LIFE! AND WHAT DO I GET IN RETURN? *DUBRAVA!*

THE INGRATES.

'SRIGHT! AND THAT SKYWALKER GREENHORN... HE GETS SHOWN AROUND, GOES ON DIPLOMATIC MISSIONS... SOAKING IN SOME AROMATIC BATH ON *JAZBINA* RIGHT NOW!

SKYWALKER?

YOU KNOW HIM?

UH... YEAH. THE INGRATE!

'SRIGHT.

IT'S OVER, SIR.

WELL DONE. TRANSMIT *CODE SILVER* TO LORD VADER--TELL HIM THE SUBJECT IS ON *JAZBINA!*

"WAIT HERE, MAKE SURE THE FIRE DOESN'T SPREAD", SAID THE CAPTAIN.

AND LOOK WHAT WE'VE FOUND!

MAYBE WE SHOULD BRING HIM WITH US?

WHAT FOR? JUST SHOOT HIM AND LET'S GO HOME!

KID...

IT'S BOBEK...

BOBEK... WHY DID YOU DO IT?... WHERE DID YOU GET THAT GUN?

I BOUGHT IT... TO KILL *YOU.*

WISH YOU HAD.

NO. HAD TO... HELP... REBELLION.

THE REB... ELLION IS BIGGER... MORE IMPORTANT THAN... YOU. THAN M--

MMUH--

IT'S A GOOD SHIP, SONNY. NOT NEW, BUT GOOD-- FROM THE OLD DAYS WHEN THEY STILL KNEW HOW TO BUILD 'EM.

IT'S GOOD FOR SHORT RUNS AND GOOD FOR HYPERJUMPS, TOO.

YOU HAVE THE LOOKS OF SOMEONE WHO'D BE NEEDING HYPERJUMPS, SONNY. EH?

BLASTERS WORKING, TOO! JUST IN CASE, EH?

YOU'VE FLOWN COMBAT BEFORE, SONNY?

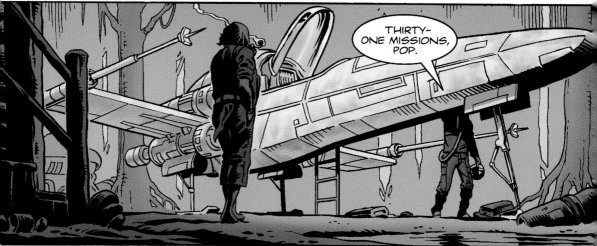

THIRTY-ONE MISSIONS, POP.

NOT ONE MORE IMPORTANT THAN THIS.

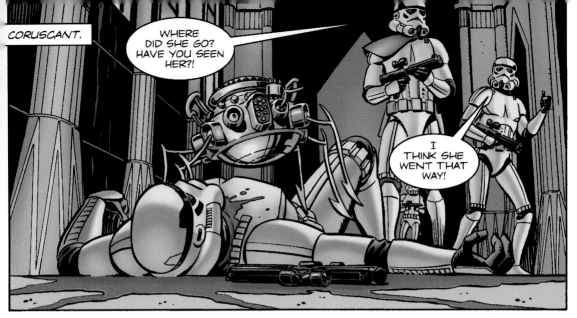

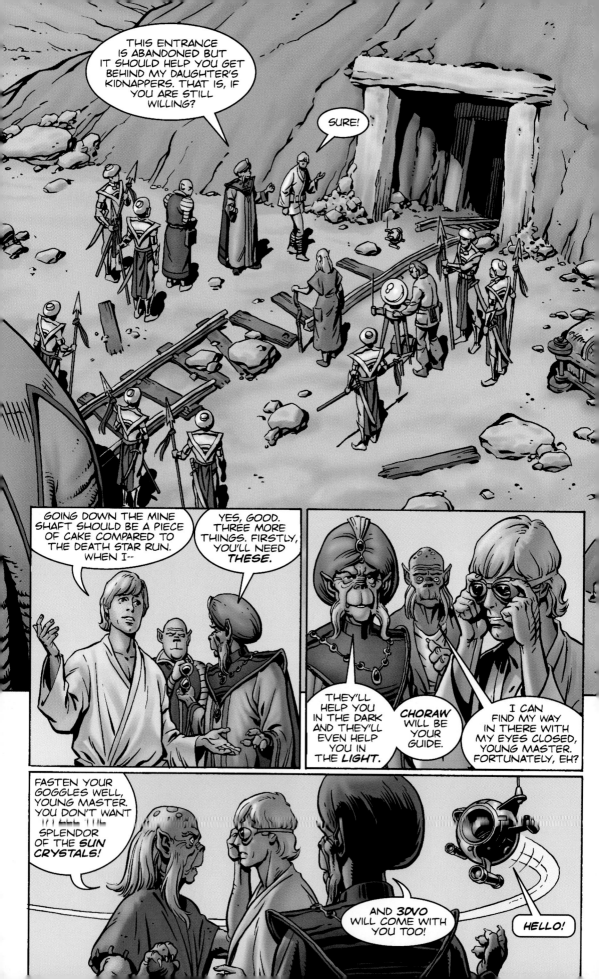

3DVO WILL RECORD YOUR HEROIC DEED, AND MY PEOPLE WILL HAVE THE PROOF OF THE REBELLION'S GOOD INTENTIONS.

HELLO YOURSELF!

DO YOU WANT TO SEE THE HOLO OF THE PRINCESS *SYAYNA* TO REFRESH YOUR MEMORY?

AND I HAVE MANY OTHER FUNCTIONS, SOME OF THEM SUPRESSED, WHILE JOURNALISTIC OBJECTIVITY IS MY PRIMARY GOAL!

YES, GOOD. NOW IF YOU'D STOP WASTING OUR TIME --

WE SHOULD GO, RIGHT? LET'S GO THEN!

TRANSMISSION IMPECCABLE, OH MAJESTIC ONE! YOU'LL BE WITH THEM EVERY STEP OF THE WAY!

GOOD.

ARE THE PEOPLE OF JAZBINA TRULY LOYAL TO THE EMPIRE, CHORAW?

I AM AN OLD MAN WHO CAN'T EVEN SEE THE STARS. HOW SHOULD I KNOW ABOUT THE FORCES THAT OWN THEM?

YEAH, BUT...I MEAN, EVEN IF THE EMPIRE PAYS YOU FOR THE ORE, THAT SHOULDN'T MEAN THEY'VE BOUGHT YOUR HEARTS--

HSST!

DO YOU HEAR THAT?

WHAT, THE *TREMORS?*

IT'S *TIKULINI!*

TIKULINI?

"THE DEATH OF A MYRIAD KNIVES" -- IT'S A FOLK NAME FOR THE *MINING WORMS!*

THEY TOLD US ALL TIKULINI WERE DEAD, BUT I KNEW THERE MUST BE ONE MORE!

IT SOUNDS LIKE A *HUGE* ONE! C'MON, LET'S *RUN!*

NO.

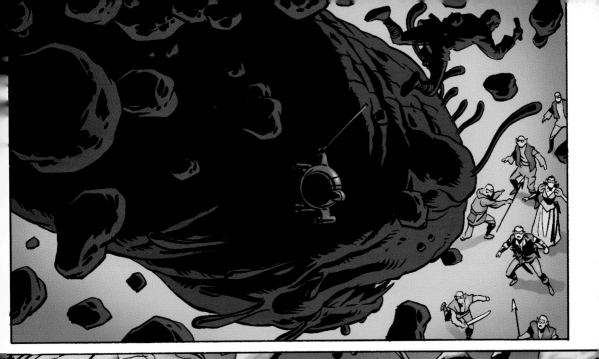

PRINCESS SYAYNA?

WHAT?!

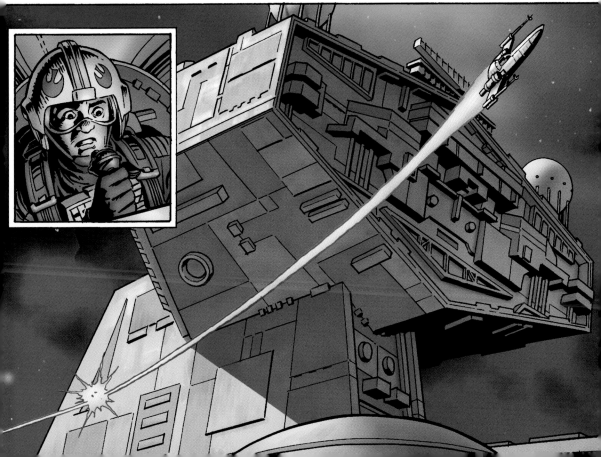

SYAYNA! GREAT NEWS!

CAN'T WAIT TO HEAR IT.

STILL CROSS WITH ME, DAUGHTER?

A PRISONER IN MY OWN HOME? WHAT NEXT?

INTOLERABLE, YOU'RE RIGHT! HERE!

BUT WAIT TILL YOU HEAR THIS -- VADER'S COMING!

LORD VADER?

YES! AND HE WANTS SKYWALKER DEAD!

IF THAT'S LORD VADER'S WISH, WE MUST NOT HESITATE! TO THE DUNGEONS!

EH?

WITH A BLASTER? SHOULDN'T WE DO IT WITH... MORE STYLE?

NO TIME! VADER WILL BE HERE ANY MOMENT! HE'LL APPRECIATE IT IF WE DO IT QUICKLY AND EFFECTIVELY!

RECORD EVERYTHING, 3DVO, EVERYTHING! AND LOCK INTO THE PUBLIC HOLO SYSTEM, I WANT EVERYONE TO SEE MY TRIUMPH!

I KNOW! I WOULDN'T MISS IT FOR THE GALAXY!

LOOK, THERE'S THE BIGWIG...WHAT-ZIZ-NAME? DARK SOMETHING?

DARTH. DARTH VADER.

HUZZAH FOR DARFADER!

I THOUGHT THE DEAL WAS NO EMPIRE HERE AS LONG AS WE SHIP 'EM ORE? WHAT NOW?

LOOK AT PREPREDENKO! POSITIVELY RADIANT!

HUZZAH FOR PERPE... PREDPRE... WHO GAVE HIM A NAME LIKE THAT?

CORUSCANT.

WE'VE GOT HER, SIR!

JAZBINA.

THE VERY CENTER OF HELL.

IT *CAN'T* BE! YOUR MESSAGE SAID... HAVE *MERCY*, LORD VADER!

DARKNESS IS YOUR CURE, SKYWALKER.

SOME MINERS GET BLINDED BY THE SUN CRYSTALS BUT MOST LOSE THEIR SIGHT BECAUSE THEY GET **ADDICTED** TO INTENSE LIGHT!

THEY STARE INTO THE SUN OR ACTIVATE MORE CRYSTALS JUST TO RELIVE THE EXPERIENCE.

STAY IN THE DARK AND YOU SHOULD BE FINE.

WHAT WAS ALL THAT ABOUT?!

WHY THE SUDDEN CONCERN ABOUT BLONDIE'S HEALTH, SYAYNA?

WHAT?

HE'S GOTTEN US INTO THIS AND YOU STILL SAVED HIM! AND NOW YOU'RE A NURSE TO HIM AND --

ARE YOU **JEALOUS**, RAOL?

DO I HAVE A REASON TO BE?

PRINCESS! THE HOLO! WE MIGHT HAVE **SOMETHING!**

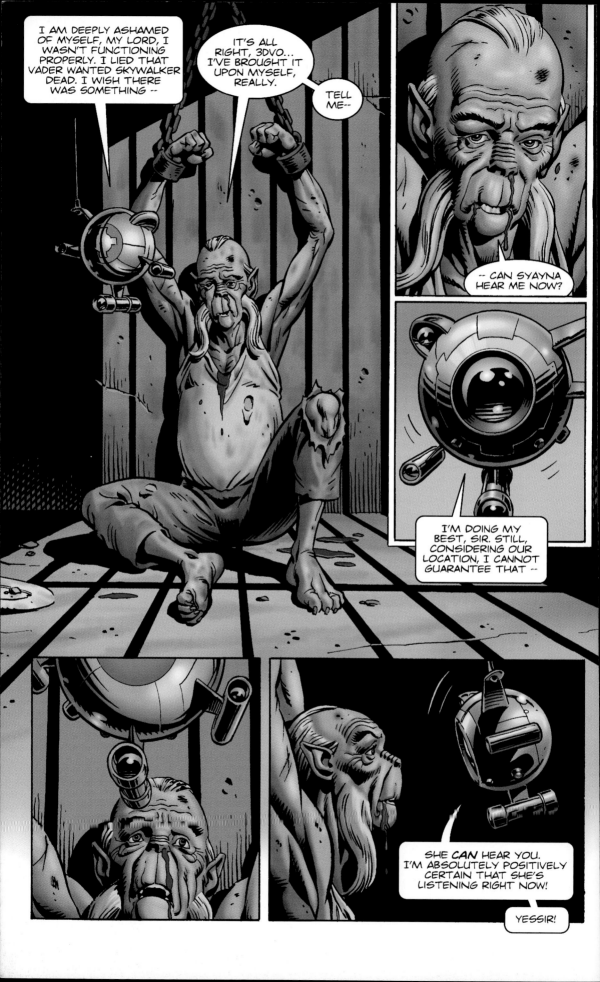

FATHER!

MY LORD?

MASTER?

THERE IT IS! SHOOT IT!

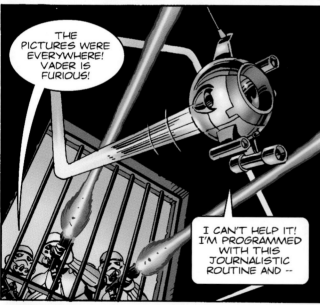

THE PICTURES WERE EVERYWHERE! VADER IS FURIOUS!

I CAN'T HELP IT! I'M PROGRAMMED WITH THIS JOURNALISTIC ROUTINE AND --

HEY, YOU MEAN THE PICS GOT OUT? I DID IT?!

THEN I'M GLAD, TOO.

RIGHT. WHAT CAN YOU DO?

'TWAS ONLY PREPREDENKO, AFTER ALL. ANOTHER ONE, SEBB?

NO, THANKS. YOU GONNA LAUGH, BUT I DON'T FEEL LIKE IT, SOMEHOW.

I AIN'T GONNA LAUGH. I *AIN'T*.

OOF!

HE'S DEAD.

THERE ARE MORE!

I'LL CHECK IN HERE!

DROP THE WEAPON!

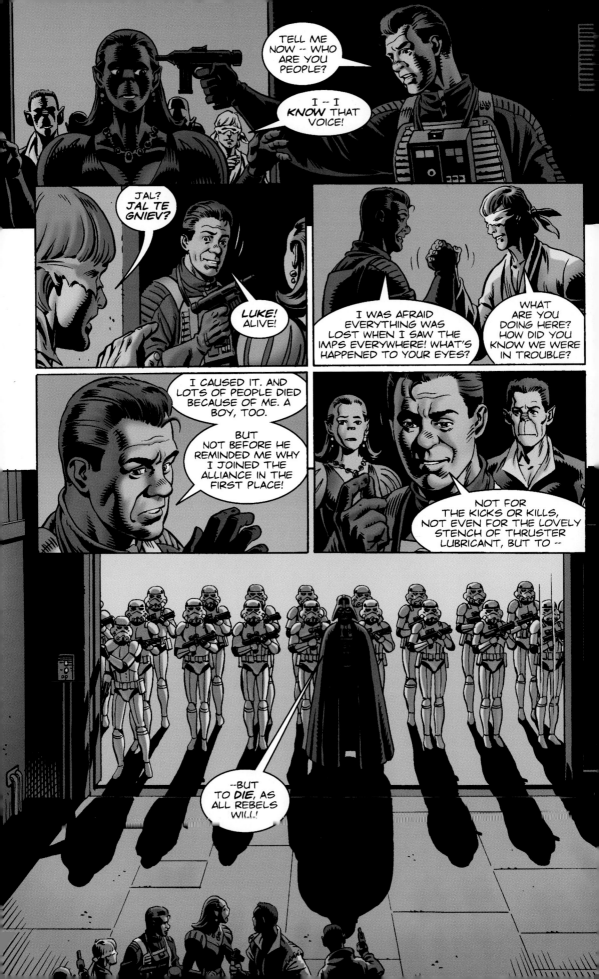

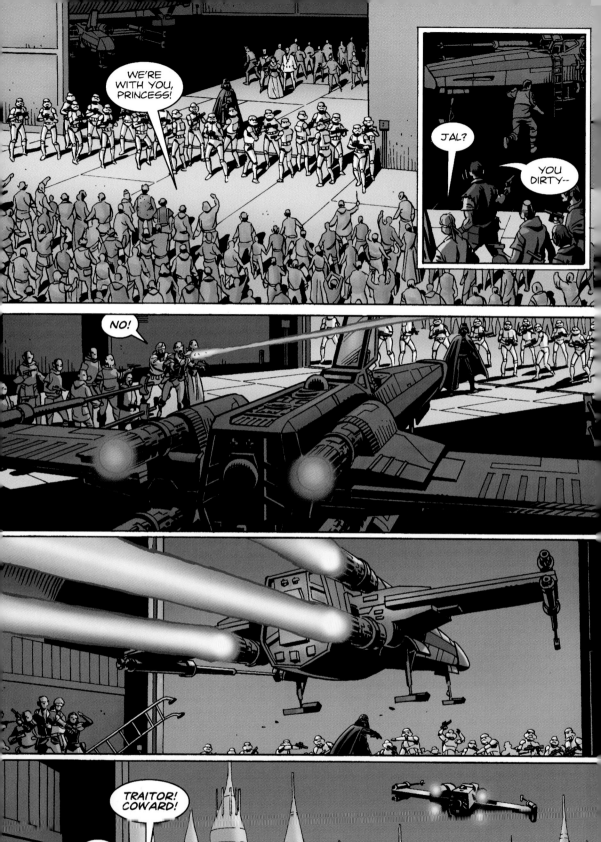

A STRAY X-WING, CAPTAIN, SIR!

OPEN SHIELD -- THE TIES WILL WANT TO HAVE THEIR FUN!

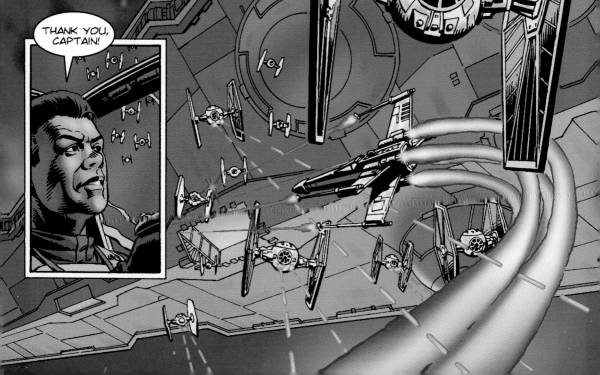

THANK YOU, CAPTAIN!

IT IS NOT OVER YET.

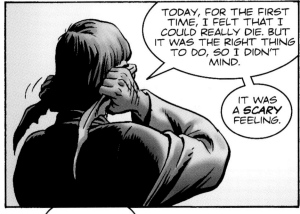

I SEE.

YOU DO REALIZE WHERE YOU ARE AND WHOSE WORD YOUR LIFE DEPENDS ON, DO YOU? WHY SHOULD I LET YOUR INSOLENCE GO UNPUNISHED?

BECAUSE IT AMUSES YOU TO DO SO?

QUITE.

WELL PLAYED, LITTLE ONE!

GO NOW. ANY MOMENT NOW MY APPRENTICE WILL COME WITH YET ANOTHER *FAILURE* TO REPORT!

HE'LL BOW AND APOLOGIZE AND OFFER ANOTHER BIT OF HIS FLESH, ALL THE TIME HIDING THE TRUTH I ALREADY KNOW.

I'LL LET HIM PLAY HIS GAME, AND I'LL PLAY IT ALONG WITH HIM, BECAUSE...IT AMUSES ME TO DO SO.

WITHIN THE GAME THERE IS A GAME AND WHEN I GREET HIM I'LL DO SO WITH THESE WORDS --

"HELLO, APPRENTICE, DARK LORD OF THE SITH. HELLO DARTH VADER. HELLO -- "

Darko Macan began his comics career in 1988, writing and drawing *Tom & Jerry* for a publisher in Darko's native Croatia. In 1989, he started writing scripts, first for a German publisher and then for the US market, for whom he has written *Grendel Tales* (two critically praised arcs with countryman Edvin Biukovic, collected as *Devils and Deaths*), *Donald Duck & Mickey Mouse*, *Tarzan*, *Tarzan/Carson of Venus*, *Aliens*, *Hellblazer*, and many more. *Vader's Quest* is not Darko's first dalliance with the dark side, having penned *X-Wing Rogue Squadron: The Phantom Affair* and upcoming stories for *Chewbacca* and *Star Wars Tales*. Back home he's still drawing strips and writing stories, scripts, and the occasional novel.

DARKO MACAN

Dave Gibbons is one of the comics industry's most highly regarded creators, having illustrated and written for the top comics publishers on both sides of the Atlantic. Dave's lengthy professional resumé includes work for *2000 A.D.* (for whom he created *Rogue Trooper*), *Dr. Who*, *Superman*, *Batman*, *Green Lantern*, *Predator*, *Aliens*, and *The Dome*. His collaborations with Alan Moore on the landmark postmodern superhero epic *The Watchmen* and with Frank Miller on three acclaimed *Martha Washington* projects have gathered countless awards and changed forever the manner in which traditional comics genres are viewed. *Vader's Quest* is Dave's first foray into the *Star Wars* mythos, a universe he will revisit with the upcoming *Chewbacca* miniseries.

DAVE GIBBONS

Angus McKie's stunning painted comics first drew widespread attention in the pages of the groundbreaking French anthology *Metal Hurlant* in 1976, followed by his acclaimed series, *So Beautiful, So Dangerous* in the pages of *Heavy Metal* magazine. One of the comics industry's digital pioneers, Angus first utilized computers on his series *The Blue Lily* for Dark Horse and then went on to create the dazzling, effects-laden colors for *Martha Washington Saves the World* and *Vader's Quest* as well as producing the computer-generated series *The Dome* with frequent co-conspirator Dave Gibbons. Angus' most recent coloring efforts appear in Bryan Talbot's acclaimed *Heart of Empire: The Legacy of Luther Arkwright* and in the upcoming *Chewbacca* project.

ANGUS McKIE

EPISODE I—THE PHANTOM MENACE

A NEW HOPE

THE EMPIRE STRIKES BACK

RETURN OF THE JEDI

THE STAR WARS TRILOGY BOXED SET

IN DEADLY PURSUIT

THE REBEL STORM

ESCAPE TO HOTH

THE EARLY ADVENTURES

HAN SOLO AT STARS' END

DARK EMPIRE

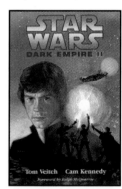

DARK EMPIRE II

EMPIRE'S END

CRIMSON EMPIRE

DEATH, LIES, & TREACHERY

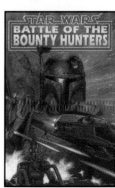

BATTLE OF THE BOUNTY HUNTERS

SOLDIER FOR THE EMPIRE HC

REBEL AGENT HC

JEDI KNIGHT HC

SOLDIER FOR THE EMPIRE

REBEL AGENT

HEIR TO THE EMPIRE

DARK FORCE RISING

THE LAST COMMAND

THE KALARBA ADVENTURES

REBELLION

SHADOWS OF THE EMPIRE

SPLINTER OF THE MIND'S EYE

DARK LORDS OF THE SITH

THE FREEDON NADD UPRISING

KNIGHTS OF THE OLD REPUBLIC

THE SITH WAR

STAR WARS BACKLIST

THE GOLDEN AGE OF THE SITH

THE FALL OF THE SITH EMPIRE

THE PHANTOM AFFAIR

BATTLEGROUND: TATOOINE

THE WARRIOR PRINCESS

REQUIEM FOR A ROGUE

IN THE EMPIRE'S SERVICE

BLOOD AND HONOR

A NEW HOPE—MANGA #1

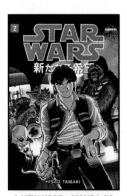

A NEW HOPE—MANGA #2

A NEW HOPE—MANGA #3

A NEW HOPE—MANGA #4

**THE EMPIRE STRIKES BACK—
MANGA #1**

**THE EMPIRE STRIKES BACK—
MANGA #2**

**THE EMPIRE STRIKES BACK—
MANGA #3**

**THE EMPIRE STRIKES BACK—
MANGA #4**